LUDWIG VAN BEETHOVEN

SYMPHONY No. 2

D major/D-Dur/Ré majeur
Op. 36

Edited by/Herausgegeben von
Richard Clarke

Ernst Eulenburg Ltd

London · Mainz · Madrid · New York · Paris · Prague · Tokyo · Toronto · Zürich

CONTENTS

BEETHOVEN'S SYMPHONIC PRODUCTION: COMPOSITION, PERFORMANCE, PUBLICATION
BEETHOVENS SINFONISCHES WERK: DATEN DER ENTSTEHUNG, URAUFFÜHRUNG, VERÖFFENTLICHUNG

	Title and key/ Titel und Tonart	(Preliminary) principal dates of composition/ (Entwürfe) Haupt-Kompositionsdaten	First performance (all in Vienna)/Uraufführung (alle in Wien)	First edition/Erstausgabe	Dedication/Widmung
Hess 298	Sinfonia, C minor/Moll (sketches/Skizzen)	? late 1780s/späte 1780er	–	–	–
–	Symphony, C	c. 1795–1797			
Op.21	Symphony No.1, C	1799–1800	Burgtheater, 2 April 1800	Hoffmeister, Vienna/ Wien, December 1801	Freiherr Gottfried van Swieten
Op.36	Symphony No.2, D	1801–1802	Theater an der Wien, 5 April 1803	Bureau of Arts and Industry, Vienna/Kunst- und Industrie-Kontor, Wien, March/März 1804	Fürst Carl von Lichnowsky
Op.55	Symphony No.3, E♭ (Sinfonia eroica)	1803–1804	Theater an der Wien, 7 April 1805	Bureau of Arts and Industry, Vienna/Kunst und Industrie-Kontor, Wien, October 1806	Fürst Franz Joseph von Lobkowitz
Op.60	Symphony No.4, B♭	1806	Palais Lobkowitz 7 March 1807	Bureau of Arts and Industry, Vienna/Kunst und Industrie-Kontor, Wien, 1808	Graf Franz von Oppersdorff
Op.67	Symphony No.5, C minor/Moll	(1804–1805) 1807–1808	Theater an der Wien, 22 December 1808	Breitkopf & Härtel, Leipzig, March/März 1809	Fürst Lobkowitz und Graf Andreas von Rasumovsky
Op.68	Symphony No.6, F (Sinfonia pastorale)	(1807) 1808	Theater an der Wien, 22 December 1808	Breitkopf & Härtel, Leipzig, May 1809	Fürst Lobkowitz und Graf Rasumovsky
Op.92	Symphony No.7, A	1811–1812	Great Hall of the University/Universitäts-Aula, 8 December 1813	Steiner, Vienna/Wien November 1816	Graf Moritz von Fries
Op.93	Symphony No.8, F	1812	Großer Redoutensaal, 27 February 1814,	Steiner, Vienna/Wien 1817	–
Op.125	Symphony No.9 D minor/ Moll ('Choral')	(1812–1822) 1823–1824	Kärntnertortheater, 7 May 1824	Schott, Mainz, August 1826	König Friedrich Wilhelm von Preußen

PREFACE

Despite the well-known tradition in Beethoven criticism of assigning the composer's works to one of three creative periods, the nine symphonies are perhaps best divided into four groups. The First and Second were written during the time that conventionally marks the transition between the early and middle period. The next four belong to what may be described as the 'heroic phase',[1] which begins in 1803 and is marked by a prodigious output of highly original works on a grand scale. The Seventh and Eighth, which mark the end of the middle period, show a certain retreat from the bold directions taken in the first six works. The Ninth is Beethoven's only symphony of the last 15 years of his life; and its unusual structure and unprecedented large performing forces place it in a category of its own.

In fact, Symphonies 1 and 2 look back to 18th-century Viennese classicism more than they foreshadow their composer's path-breaking achievements in the genre; the Second, in particular, enjoys a close kinship with Mozart's 'Prague' Symphony (K504) of 1786, a work with which it shares tonality, mood, and the shape of the slow introduction to the first movement. The *Eroica* was begun immediately after the Second, but under profoundly different personal circumstances for its composer: it is the first work in which he came to terms with his increasing deafness by going far beyond the limits of musical convention. The next symphony Beethoven began composing, in C minor (the Fifth), took the genre a stage further by its concern for overall planning, its four contrasting movements being 'unified' by the presence – at different levels – of the parallel tonality of C major. In the *Sinfonia pastorale* (the Sixth) he solved the problem of large-scale organisation in other ways, by joining the last three movements to one another and by drawing a dynamic curve across the entire work.

Beethoven's progress as a symphonist did not pursue a single path, or a straight line, as seems to have been the case in the string quartets. The Fourth Symphony, which was composed quickly in the summer of 1806 and represents something of a return to classical principles (the orchestral forces required for it are the smallest for a Beethoven symphony), may have been released before the Fifth on account of unfavourable reactions to the *Eroica* after its first performance in 1805. It is more likely that memories of the artistic failure of the first concert featuring the Fifth and Sixth Symphonies prompted the composer to write a pair of musically lighter works, or at least cooler ones, in 1811–12; more than the Fourth Symphony, the Eighth marks a return to 18th-century symphonic dimensions.

With the Ninth, of course, Beethoven resumed his pioneering role as a symphonist, combining a supreme command of sonata structures and orchestral technique with masterly control of the additional forces of chorus and solo voices to shape a type of composition hitherto unknown in serious concert music. This fusion of symphony and oratorio was by no means quickly realized. The intention to write a symphony in D minor was first expressed during the composition of the Eighth; the theme of the Scherzo was first sketched a few years later in 1815; the first sketchleaf entry describing a symphony with chorus dates from 1818.[2] By the time the Ninth was completed 12 years had elapsed since the previous symphonies; only the composition of a still more innovatory set of works, the late string quartets, remained to be achieved.

---

[1] The expression was coined by Alan Tyson (in his essay 'Beethoven's Heroic Phase', *The Musical Times*, CX (1969), 139–41) in connection with the years 1803–5, which saw the composition of the *Eroica*, the oratorio *Christus am Ölberge* ('The Mount of Olives'), and the opera *Leonore*; but the period may be extended to include the major instrumental works that followed in their wake.

[2] For a full account of the early plans for Beethoven's last symphony, see Sieghard Brandenburg, 'Die Skizzen zur Neunten Symphonie', *Zu Beethoven* 2, ed. H. Goldschmidt (Berlin, 1984), 88–129

Towards the end of his life Beethoven expressed the desire to write one more symphony. Two of his companions from the late years, Anton Schindler and Karl Holz, claimed that large sections of a 'Tenth Symphony' had been sketched and that the work was complete in the composer's mind; but from the evidence of the surviving manuscripts, it appears that little, if any, progress was made on a new work in the genre.[3]

From the point of view of performance and early reception, it is not the year 1803, but 1807 that marks the dividing line in Beethoven's symphonic output. The first four symphonies were originally intended more for private consumption, being written for and dedicated to their patrons and played mainly in aristocratic circles. The last five symphonies were written specifically for public concerts. The Fifth and Sixth, composed in 1813–14, were heard for the first time in December 1808; the Seventh and Eighth (also composed in rapid succession) at a series of concerts in the winter of 1807–8. For each pair of works, Beethoven composed – nearer the date of the concerts – an occasional piece that would provide a fitting end to a musically arduous programme; the Choral Fantasy in 1808, the 'Battle Symphony' (*Wellingtons Sieg*) in 1813. When the Ninth Symphony was first performed in May 1824, in a programme that included other Viennese Beethoven premieres, its own finale provided the rousing conclusion to the concert.

SYMPHONY No. 2

Beethoven began to draft his Second Symphony in the winter of 1800/1, following the success of his First Symphony the previous spring. But it proved more difficult to compose: after devoting more time to it the following winter, he was able to work intensively on it in the summer and early autumn of 1802, which he spent at Heiligenstadt. He finished the score soon after writing out the famous letter to his brothers Johann and Caspar Carl, known as the Heiligenstadt Testament, in which he struggled to express the social suffering brought on by deafness, and the artistic ideals he was to embrace as a way of enduring it. The sketches for the work are mainly in two manuscripts, both of which have been published in critical editions.[4]

The work was first performed at the Theater an der Wien on 5 April 1803, at a concert that also included the First Symphony and the first performances of the Piano Concerto No.3 in C minor and the oratorio *Christus am Ölberge* ('The Mount of Olives'). It was admired for its 'surprising and brilliant passages of beauty',[5] but was less well liked than the First Symphony.

Beethoven offered the symphony to Breitkopf & Härtel in Leipzig as early as March 1802 and, after failing to agree on a price, to Johann André in Offenbach in November; after these negotiations came to nothing, he repeated his offer to Breitkopf in January 1803. The symphony was ultimately published (in parts) in March 1804 by the Bureau of Arts and Industry in Vienna. An unauthorized full score was published in London in November and December 1808; Simrock of Bonn issued the first German score, with the composer's knowledge and tacit approval, in 1822.

The symphony was dedicated to one of Beethoven's most important early patrons and closest friends, Prince Carl von Lichnowsky, who had previously been the recipient of the composer's opus 1 (a set of three piano trios)

---

[3] The problems of the 'Tenth' are summarized and discussed by Robert Winter in an essay (in English) entitled 'Noch einmal: wo sind Beethovens Skizzen zur Zehnten Symphonie?', in *Beethoven-Jahrbuch*, X (1977), 531–2

[4] Berlin, Staatsbibliothek Preussischer Kulturbesitz, mus.ms.autogr.Beethoven Landsberg 7, transcribed by Karl Lothar Mikulicz as *Ein Notierungsbuch von Beethoven*, Leipzig 1927; reprinted Hildesheim 1972. Vienna, Gesellschaft der Musikfreunde, manuscript A34, published in facsimile and transcription by Sieghard Brandenburg as *Ludwig van Beethoven: Kesslersches Skizzenbuch*, 2vols., Bonn 1976–8. Brandenburg's edition supersedes Gustav Nottebohm's selective transcriptions in *Ein Skizzenbuch von Beethoven*, Leipzig 1865. An account of the genesis of the work, relying exclusively on transcriptions made by Mikulicz (and earlier by Nottebohm) is given in Kurt Westphal's *Vom Einfall zur Symphonie: Einblick in Beethovens Schaffensweise*, Berlin 1965.

[5] *Zeitung für die elegante Welt*, quoted in A.W.Thayer, *Thayer's Life of Beethoven*, rev. and ed. Elliot Forbes, Princeton 1964, 330

and two of his most innovatory piano sonatas (the *Pathétique* Op.13, and the A flat major Op.26). Beethoven's pupil Ferdinand Ries recalled that Lichnowsky had been present at the disastrous dress rehearsal for the premiere, on the morning of 5 April, and had large baskets of food and wine brought to the theatre to revive the participants and restore their good humour.[6]

The Second Symphony has always been a popular work in the concert hall, but has failed to attract much analytical or critical discussion.[7] It is a more polished work than the First, but lacks the harmonic audacity of the opening chord of the slow introduction to the earlier work. And, of course, it falls short of the *Eroica*, the Fifth and the *Pastoral* in scope and originality: Maynard Solomon has fittingly called it 'the work of a mature master who is settling accounts – or making peace – with the high-Classic symphonic tradition before embarking on an unprecedented musical voyage'.[8]

William Drabkin

---

[6] Franz Gerhard Wegeler and Ferdinand Ries, *Biographische Notizen über Ludwig van Beethoven*, Koblenz 1838, suppl. 1845, 75–6

[7] In his essay 'Structural Relations between Op.28 and Op.36' (*Beethoven Studies 2*, ed. A.Tyson, London 1977, 66–83), Daniel Coren has noted the absence of informed comment on the D major Piano Sonata referred to in the title; but, as his scant references to the secondary literature show, the symphony is in a similar position.

[8] Maynard Solomon, *Beethoven*, New York 1977, 104

VORWORT

Obwohl nunmehr traditionell Beethovens Schaffen in drei Perioden eingeteilt wird, ist es wahrscheinlich treffender, die neun Sinfonien in vier Gruppen zu untergliedern. Die erste und zweite Sinfonie entstanden zu einer Zeit, die nach allgemeiner Einschätzung den Übergang zwischen früher und mittlerer Periode darstellt. Die folgenden vier kann man einer „heroischen Phase"[1] zuordnen, die sich, 1803 beginnend, durch eine beachtliche Produktion von in höchstem Maße originären Werken großen Umfangs auszeichnet. Die „Siebte" und „Achte" als Abschluss der mittleren Periode lassen einen gewissen Rückzug von den kühnen Wegen erkennen, die er in den ersten sechs Werken dieser Gattung eingeschlagen hatte. Die „Neunte" ist Beethovens einzige Sinfonie der letzten 15 Lebensjahre; ihre außergewöhnliche Gesamtform und nie vorher dagewesene Aufführungsdauer machen sie zu einem Sonderfall.

Die Sinfonien 1 und 2 sind in der Tat eher eine Rückschau auf die Wiener Klassik des 18. Jahrhunderts, als dass sie die bahnbrechenden Errungenschaften des Komponisten in der Gattung erkennen ließen: Besonders die „Zweite" zeigt eine enge Verwandtschaft mit Mozarts „Prager" Sinfonie KV 504 aus dem Jahre 1786, mit der sie Tonart, Grundstimmung und das Vorhandensein einer langsamen Einleitung zum 1. Satz gemein hat. Die „Eroica" wurde unmittelbar nach der „Zweiten" in Angriff genommen, jedoch unter grundsätzlich veränderten persönlichen Umständen für den Komponisten: Sie war sein erstes Werk, worin er sich mit seiner fortschreitenden Ertaubung arrangierte, indem er die Grenzen der musikalischen Konvention weit hinter sich ließ. Die nächste Sinfonie, die

Beethoven zu komponieren begann, stand in c-Moll (die spätere „Fünfte") und war in Anbetracht der satzübergreifenden Anlage, deren vier kontrastierende Sätze durch die differenzierte Präsenz der gleichnamigen Dur-Tonart C-Dur miteinander verklammert werden, ein großer Schritt in der Weiterentwicklung der Gattung. In der „Sechsten", der *Sinfonia pastorale*, kam Beethoven hinsichtlich der großformatigen Gliederung zu einer ganz anderen Lösung, indem er einerseits die letzten drei Sätze miteinander verband und andererseits das gesamte Werk mit einem wirksamen Gestaltungsbogen überzog.

Beethovens Fortgang als Sinfoniker lässt sich nicht als Einbahnstraße oder als gerade Linie verfolgen, wie es sich für das Streichquartettschaffen anbietet. Die vierte Sinfonie, im Sommer 1806 schnell hingeworfen, scheint zu den Ursprüngen der Klassik zurückzukehren – so ist beispielsweise die Orchesterbesetzung von allen Beethoven-Sinfonien die kleinste – und hat vermutlich aufgrund der mehr als zurückhaltenden Reaktion auf die Uraufführung der „Eroica" (1805) vor ihr den Vorzug der früheren öffentlichen Präsentation erhalten. Noch wahrscheinlicher ist die Annahme, Beethoven habe in Anbetracht des künstlerischen Misserfolgs der Erstaufführung von fünfter und sechster Sinfonie sich dazu veranlasst gesehen, in den Jahren 1811/12 ein Paar von musikalisch unbeschwerteren oder gar zurückhaltenderen Werken zu komponieren; mehr noch als die „Vierte" kehrt schließlich die achte Sinfonie zu der üblichen Ausdehnung einer Sinfonie des 18. Jahrhunderts zurück.

Mit der neunten Sinfonie hatte Beethoven natürlich die Rolle als sinfonischer Vorkämpfer für sich zurückgewonnen, indem er den höchsten Anspruch an Sonatenhauptsatzform und orchestrale Mittel mit meisterhafter Beherrschung des Potentials von Chor und Solostimmen verband und so einen Kompositionstyp

---

[1] Der Ausdruck wurde geprägt von Alan Tyson in seinem Essay „Beethoven's Heroic Phase", in: *The Musical Times*, CX (1969), S. 139–141, mit Bezug auf die Jahre 1803–1805, während derer die „Eroica", das Oratorium *Christus am Ölberge* op. 85 und die Oper *Leonore* komponiert wurden. Doch kann man diese Schaffensperiode ebenso erweitern und die in den folgenden Jahren entstandenen instrumentalen Hauptwerke einbeziehen.

schuf, der bis dahin in der ernsten konzertanten Musik ohnegleichen war. Diese Verquickung von Sinfonie und Oratorium war indes von langer Hand vorbereitet. Erste Anzeichen zur Komposition einer d-Moll-Sinfonie gab es zur Zeit der Niederschrift der „Achten"; das Thema des Scherzos in seiner ursprünglichen Gestalt wurde 1815, wenige Jahre später, skizziert; das erste Skizzenblatt, das den Hinweis auf eine Sinfonie mit Chor enthält, datiert von 1818.[2] Bis zur Vollendung der „Neunten" waren seit den vorangegangenen Sinfonien zwölf Jahre verstrichen, und lediglich eine noch umwälzendere Reihe von Werken harrte ihrer Vollendung: die späten Streichquartette.

Gegen Ende seines Lebens äußerte sich Beethoven über sein Streben nach der Komposition einer weiteren Sinfonie. Zwei seiner Wegbegleiter in den letzten Jahren, Anton Schindler und Karl Holz, stellten die Behauptung auf, dass weite Teile einer zehnten Sinfonie in Skizzen existierten und dass das Werk im Kopf des Komponisten vollständig entworfen worden wäre. Jedoch erscheinen die überlieferten Skizzen vergleichsweise unbedeutend, da sie zu geringe, wenn überhaupt irgendwelche, Fortschritte zur Vollendung eines neuen Werkes in dieser Gattung erkennen lassen.[3]

Aus der Sicht von Aufführung und früher Rezeption markiert nicht das Jahr 1803, sondern 1807 die Trennlinie in Beethovens Schaffen. Die ersten vier Sinfonien waren eigentlich mehr für den privaten Gebrauch bestimmt: für ihre Förderer geschrieben, ihnen gewidmet und vornehmlich in aristokratischen Kreisen aufgeführt. Demgegenüber sollten die letzten fünf Sinfonien ausdrücklich dem breiten Publikum vorgestellt werden. Die 1807/08 komponierten Sinfonien Nr. 5 und 6 erlebten ihre Uraufführung im Dezember 1808, die in ebenfalls rascher

Aufeinanderfolge niedergeschriebenen Sinfonien Nr. 7 und 8 in einer Folge von Konzerten während des Winters 1813/14. Als Ergänzung zu jedem Werkpaar komponierte Beethoven kurz vor der Aufführung ein Gelegenheitswerk, das ein musikalisch anspruchsvolles Programm zu einem quasi versöhnlichen Ende führen sollte: 1808 war es die Chorfantasie op. 80, 1813 die „Schlacht- und Siegessinfonie" (*Wellingtons Sieg oder die Schlacht bei Vittoria*) op. 91. Im Mai 1824, als die neunte Sinfonie neben anderen Wiener Uraufführungen von Werken Beethovens dem Publikum vorgestellt wurde, war es ihr eigenes Finale, das den krönenden Abschluss der Veranstaltung darstellte.

SINFONIE Nr. 2

Im Winter 1800/01, im Sog des Erfolges seiner 1. Sinfonie vom vorangegangenen Frühling, begann Beethoven mit den Entwürfen zur 2. Sinfonie. Allerdings erwies sich das Komponieren bald als nicht eben einfach. Nach weiteren Arbeiten an diesem Werk fand er erst im Sommer und im Frühherbst 1802 Gelegenheit, sich intensiv mit ihm zu beschäftigen. Zu dieser Zeit hielt er sich in Heiligenstadt auf. Er schloss die Niederschrift der Partitur in kurzem Abstand nach dem als Heiligenstädter Testament bekannten Brief an seine Brüder Johann und Caspar Carl ab, jenem berühmten Brief, in dem er sich verzweifelt darum bemühte, die durch zunehmende Taubheit hervorgerufenen sozialen Leiden aufzuzeigen und die künstlerischen Ideale zu formulieren, die er in sich aufnehmen müsste, um diese Last tragen zu können. Im Wesentlichen sind die Skizzen zur 2. Sinfonie in zwei Manuskripten niedergelegt, die beide in kritischen Ausgaben veröffentlicht wurden.[4]

---

2 Hinsichtlich einer vollständigen Darstellung der frühen Pläne zu Beethovens letzter Sinfonie vgl. Sieghard Brandenburg, „Die Skizzen zur Neunten Symphonie", in: *Zu Beethoven 2*, hg. v. Harry Goldschmidt, Berlin 1984, S. 88–129.

3 Die Problematik der „Zehnten" ist aufgeführt und zusammengefasst von Robert Winter in einem in englischer Sprache verfassten und mit „Noch einmal: wo sind Beethovens Skizzen zur Zehnten Symphonie?" betitelten Aufsatz in *Beethoven-Jahrbuch X* (1977), S. 531–552.

4 Berlin, Staatsbibliothek Preußischer Kulturbesitz, mus. ms. autogr. Beethoven Landsberg 7, übertragen von Karl Lothar Mikulicz als *Ein Notierungsbuch von Beethoven*, Leipzig 1927, Reprint Hildesheim 1972. Wien, Gesellschaft der Musikfreunde, Manuskript A 34, faksimiliert und übertragen von Sieghard Brandenburg als *Ludwig van Beethoven: Kesslersches Skizzenbuch*, 2 Bde., Bonn 1976/78. Brandenburgs Ausgabe ersetzt die auszugsweisen Übertragungen Gustav Nottebohms in *Ein Skizzenbuch von Beethoven*, Leipzig 1865. In *Vom Einfall zur Symphonie: Einblick in Beethovens Schaffensweise*, Berlin

Das Werk erlebte seine Uraufführung am 5. April 1803 im Theater an der Wien. Auf dem Programm standen außerdem die 1. Sinfonie und zwei weitere Uraufführungen: die des Klavierkonzerts Nr. 3 in c-Moll und des Oratoriums *Christus am Ölberge*. Die Sinfonie wurde bewundert, weil es ihr „an auffallenden und brillanten Stellen nicht mangelt[e]"[5], aber doch nicht so wohlgefällig wie die 1. Sinfonie aufgenommen.

Schon im März 1802 bot Beethoven die Sinfonie dem Verlag Breitkopf & Härtel an. Als es aber zu keiner Einigung über das Honorar kam, wandte er sich im November an André in Offenbach und erneuerte nach dem Scheitern der Verhandlungen seine Offerte an Breitkopf im Januar 1803. Letztendlich wurde die Sinfonie in Stimmen im März 1804 vom Kunst- und Industrie-Kontor in Wien veröffentlicht. Eine nicht autorisierte Ausgabe der Partitur erschien im November/Dezember 1808 in London; bei Simrock in Bonn kam die erste Partitur in Deutschland heraus, und zwar im Jahre 1822 mit dem Wissen und stillschweigendem Einverständnis des Komponisten.

Widmungsträger wurde einer der wichtigsten frühen Förderer Beethovens und einer seiner engsten Freunde, Fürst Carl von Lichnowsky, Dieser war zuvor schon Empfänger von Beethovens opus 1 (den drei Klaviertrios) und zwei der innovatorischsten Klaviersonaten: der *Sonate pathétique*, op. 13, und der Sonate As-Dur, op. 26. Von Beethovens Schüler Ferdinand Ries stammt der Bericht, dass Lichnowsky bei der katastrophalen Hauptprobe für die 2. Sinfonie am Morgen des 5. April zugegen war. Er hatte große Körbe voll Lebensmittel und Wein ins Theater mitgebracht, um die Beteiligten zu erfrischen und bei Laune zu halten.[6]

Zwar wurde die 2. Sinfonie im Konzertsaal stets gern gehört, ist aber nie so recht zum Gegenstand analytischer oder kritischer Betrachtungen geworden.[7] Sie wirkt glatter als die „Erste", wartet nicht mit der harmonischen Kühnheit des Eröffnungsakkords in der langsamen Einleitung zum früheren Werk auf. Und es mangelt ihr – natürlich –, gemessen an der *Eroica*, der „Fünften" und der *Pastorale*, an Tragweite und Originalität. Maynard Solomon hat diese Sinfonie treffend als „das Werk eines zur Reife gelangten Meisters" bezeichnet, „der mit der hochklassischen Sinfonie-Tradition seine Rechnung begleicht – oder mit ihr Frieden schließt bevor er zu einer beispiellosen musikalischen Reise aufbricht".[8]

William Drabkin
Übersetzung: Norbert Henning

1965, gibt Kurt Westphal eine Darstellung der Entstehungsgeschichte dieses Werks und bezieht sich dabei ausschließlich auf die Übertragungen von Mikulicz (und die früheren von Nottebohm).

[5] *Zeitung für die elegante Welt*, zitiert nach A. W. Thayer, *Ludwig van Beethovens Leben*, deutsch bearbeitet von Hermann Deiters, neu ergänzt von Hugo Riemann, II, Leipzig ³1922, S. 387.

[6] Franz Gerhard Wegeler und Ferdinand Ries, *Biographische Notizen über Ludwig van Beethoven*, Koblenz 1838, ergänzte Auflage 1845, S. 75f.

[7] Daniel Coren hat in seinem Essay „Structural Relations between Op. 28 and Op. 36" (*Beethoven Studies 2*, hg. v. A. Tyson, London 1977) festgehalten, dass es keinen erhellenden Kommentar zur D-Dur-Klaviersonate gibt, auf die im Titel Bezug genommen wird; doch selbst seine knappen Verweise auf die Sekundärliteratur zeigen auf, dass die Sinfonie von einer vergleichbaren Grundhaltung bestimmt ist.

[8] Maynard Solomon, *Beethoven*, New York 1977, S. 104.

SYMPHONY No. 2

Ludwig van Beethoven
(1770–1827)
Op. 36

I. **Adagio** (♪ = 84)

Edited by Richard Clarke
© 2015 Ernst Eulenburg Ltd, London
and Ernst Eulenburg & Co GmbH, Mainz

5

13

II. Larghetto (♪ = 92)

34

III. Scherzo

Allegro ($\bullet$ = 100)

Scherzo da capo

IV. **Allegro molto** ($\downarrow$ = 152)

84